advance
pitch

FIRST PAST THE POST®

Verbal Reasoning:

Vocabulary

Multiple Choice

Book 3

advance
pitch

How to use this book to make the most of 11 plus exam preparation

It is important to remember that for 11 plus exams there is no national syllabus, no pass mark and no retake option. It is therefore vitally important that your child is fully primed in order to perform to the best of their ability to give themselves the best possible chance on the day.

Verbal reasoning tests

Verbal reasoning tests consist of short timed tests with a mixture of verbal reasoning questions. Logic, vocabulary and time management skills are assessed in these practice tests.

Never has it been more useful to learn from mistakes!

Students can improve by as much as 15 percent, not only by focused practice, but also by targeting any weak areas.

How to manage your child's own practice

To get the most up-to-date information, visit our website, www.elevenplusexams.co.uk, the UK's largest online resource for 11 plus, with over 65,000 webpages and a forum administered by a select group of experienced moderators.

About the authors

The Eleven Plus Exams' **First Past the Post®** series has been created by a team of experienced tutors and authors from leading British universities.

Published by University of Buckingham Press

With special thanks to the children who tested our material at the Eleven Plus Exams centre in Harrow.

ISBN: 9781908684844

About Us

Eleven Plus Exams is the largest website in the UK that specifically prepares children for the 11 plus exams. The website offers a vast amount of information and advice on the 11 plus as well as a moderated online forum, books, downloadable material and online services to enhance your child's chances of success.

The company also provides specialist 11 plus tuition and is a supplier of online services to schools.

Eleven Plus Exams is recognised as a trusted and authoritative source. It has been quoted in numerous national newspapers, including The Telegraph, The Observer, The Daily Mail and The Sunday Telegraph, as well as BBC Radio and national television (BBC1 and Channel 4).

Set up in 2004, the website grew from an initial 20 webpages to more than 65,000 today, and has been visited by millions of parents. The website gives impartial advice on exam preparation and techniques. It is moderated by over 20 experts who provide support for parents both before and after the exams.

Visit our website and see why we are the market's leading one-stop shop for all your 11 plus needs.

- ✓ Comprehensive quality content and advice written by 11 plus experts

- ✓ Eleven Plus Exams online shop supplying a wide range of practice books, e-papers, software and apps

- ✓ Lots of FREE practice papers to download

- ✓ Professional tuition service

- ✓ Short revision courses

- ✓ Year-long 11 plus courses

- ✓ Mock exams tailored to reflect those of the main examining bodies

Other titles in the First Past The Post® Series

11+ Essentials Range of Books

VERBAL REASONING

ISBN	TITLE
9781908684288	Verbal Reasoning: Cloze Tests Book 1
9781908684356	Verbal Reasoning: Cloze Tests Book 2
9781908684639	Verbal Reasoning: Vocabulary Book 1 - Multiple Choice
9781908684783	Verbal Reasoning: Vocabulary Book 2 - Multiple Choice
9781908684844	Verbal Reasoning: Vocabulary Book 3 - Multiple Choice
9781908684646	Verbal Reasoning: Grammar and Spelling Book 1 - Multiple Choice
9781908684790	Verbal Reasoning: Grammar and Spelling Book 2 - Multiple Choice
9781908684868	Verbal Reasoning: Vocabulary in Context Level 1
9781908684875	Verbal Reasoning: Vocabulary in Context Level 2
9781908684882	Verbal Reasoning: Vocabulary in Context Level 3
9781908684889	Verbal Reasoning: Vocabulary in Context Level 4

ENGLISH

ISBN	TITLE
9781908684295	English: Comprehensions Book 1 Classic Literature
9781908684486	English: Comprehensions Book 2 Contemporary Literature
9781908684851	English: Comprehensions Book 3 Non-Fiction

NUMERICAL REASONING

ISBN	TITLE
9781908684431	Numerical Reasoning: Quick-Fire Book 1
9781908684448	Numerical Reasoning: Quick-Fire Book 2
9781908684653	Numerical Reasoning: Quick-Fire Book 1 - Multiple Choice
9781908684752	Numerical Reasoning: Quick-Fire Book 2 - Multiple Choice
9781908684301	Numerical Reasoning: Multi-Part Book 1
9781908684363	Numerical Reasoning: Multi-Part Book 2
9781908684769	Numerical Reasoning: Multi-Part Book 1 - Multiple Choice
9781908684776	Numerical Reasoning: Multi-Part Book 2 - Multiple Choice

MATHEMATICS

ISBN	TITLE
9781908684462	Maths: Mental Arithmetic Book 1
9781908684806	Maths: Worded Problems Book 1
9781908684936	Maths: Worded Problems Book 2
9781908684493	Maths Dictionary Plus

NON-VERBAL REASONING

ISBN	TITLE
9781908684318	3D Non-Verbal Reasoning Book 1
9781908684479	3D Non-Verbal Reasoning Book 2

PUZZLES

ISBN	TITLE
9781908684905	Puzzles: Maths Crosswords
9781908684912	Puzzles: Vocabulary

Test Paper Packs

ISBN	TITLE
9781908684103	English Practice Papers - Multiple Choice Pack 1
9781908684127	Verbal Reasoning Practice Papers - Multiple Choice Pack 1
9781908684134	Non-Verbal Reasoning Practice Papers - Multiple Choice Pack 1
9781908684110	Mathematics Practice Papers - Multiple Choice Pack 1

Contents

Test 1 - Synonyms: Word Bank   1

Test 2 - Synonyms: Sentence Completion   5

Test 3 - Synonyms: Similar Words   9

Test 4 - Antonyms: Word Bank   13

Test 5 - Antonyms: Sentence Completion   17

Test 6 - Antonyms: Opposite Words   21

Test 7 - Word Definitions   25

Test 8 - Category Fit   31

Test 9 - Mixed Test   37

Test 10 - Mixed Test   43

Test 11 - Mixed Test   51

Test 12 - Mixed Test   57

Answers   65

BLANK PAGE

FIRST PAST THE POST®

Synonyms:

Word Bank

Test 1

Total
/40

You have **10** minutes to complete this test of **40** questions.

Test 1 - Synonyms: Word Bank

Choose a word from the word bank that has the meaning most similar to the word on the left.

Word Bank				
howl	sudden	deviate	jaunty	knowledgeable
immaculate	locate	rotten	aromatic	aim
cargo	refined	authentic	villainous	classification
brutal	melancholy	bizarre	success	intense

1 neat _immaculate_

2 yell _howl_

3 putrid _rotten_

4 cheerful _jaunty_

5 abrupt _sudden_

6 strive _aim_

7 wise _knowledgable_

8 find _locate_

9 fragrant _aromatic_

10 diverge _deviate_

11 peculiar _bizzare_

12 wicked _villainous_

13 freight _cargo_

14 sombre _melancholy_

15 sophisticated _refined_

16 vicious _brutal_

17 vivid _intense_

18 triumph _success_

19 genuine _authentic_

20 category _classification_

Word Bank

belligerent	~~deferential~~	courageous	deplorable	indignant
obliterate	desolation	~~friendly~~	graceful	absurd
nimble	~~pressing~~ ?	necessary ?	thrifty	monotonous
mimic	hindrance	~~healthy~~	surplus	uncover

1 **aggrieved**   ~~deferential~~ ✗ indignant

2 **swift**   nimble ✓

3 **respectful**   ~~friendly~~ ✗ deferential

4 **aggressive**   belligerent ✓

5 **emulate**   mimic ✓

6 **heroic**   courageous ✓

7 **impediment**   hindrance ✓

8 **disgraceful**   deplorable ✓

9 **ludicrous**   absurd ✓

10 **expunge**   desolation ✗ obliterate

11 **devastation**   desolation obliterate ✗

12 **obligatory**   necessary ✓

13 **expose**   uncover

14 **frugal**   thrifty

15 **excess**   surplus

16 **elegant**   graceful

17 **genial**   friendly ~~genial~~ ✓

18 **mundane**   monotonous

19 **nutritious**   healthy ✓

20 **urgent**   pressing ✓

16 / 20

BLANK PAGE

FIRST PAST THE POST®

Synonyms:

Sentence Completion

Test 2

Total

/20

You have **8** minutes to complete this test of **20** questions.

Test 2 - Synonyms: Sentence Completion

Circle the letter corresponding to the word that is most similar in meaning to the word IN CAPITALS in the sentence above.

Example	The girl **SMILED** at her friend.				
	A	B	Ⓒ	D	E
	laughed	frowned	grinned	glowered	sneered

1   **NERVOUSLY**, Jerry entered the haunted house.

A	B	C	D	Ⓔ
greedily	gracefully	solemnly	promptly	anxiously

2   She **BRANDISHED** her sword in order to fight the dragon.

A	B	Ⓒ	D	E
concealed	sharpened	wielded	crafted	damaged

3   Their **CONSTANT** squabbling meant that I had to leave the house.

A	Ⓑ	C	D	E
unfathomable	persistent	egotistical	floundering	disguised

4   Our ship had no support and was very **VULNERABLE** to enemy fire.

A	B	C	Ⓓ	E
danger	outlandish	scorn	exposed	translucent

5   I was **IMPATIENT** so I decided to skip the queue.

Ⓐ	B	C	D	E
restless	lenient	resourceful	trustworthy	opposing

6   The King's armour was very **DURABLE**.

A	B	Ⓒ	D	E
hardening	succulent	robust	sympathetic	fragile

7   I found it **AMUSING** that the clown tripped over.

A	B	C	D	E
fanatical	sumptuous	exhausting	ridicule	(E) hilarious

8   The **TANTALISING** aroma from the kitchen spread through the whole house.

A	B	C	D	E
pungent	glowing	gleeful	(D) enticing	potent

9   I **SAUNTERED** through the woods before sunset.

A	B	C	D	E
(A) strolled	sprinted	sneaked	lunged	plummeted

10   Oscar **NEGOTIATED** with his father to be allowed to go to the party.

A	B	C	D	E
fussed	bickered	squabbled	(D) bargained	argued

11   Lucy **STRIVED** to finish her coursework before the concert.

A	B	C	D	E
(A) endeavoured	forgot	neglected	failed	started

12   Daisy had a **GLIMMER** of hope that her parents would let her adopt a kitten.

A	B	C	D	E
light	candle	stutter	glitter	(E) flicker

13   She **STORMED** out of the room after the argument with her father.

A	B	C	D	E
lightening	lighted	(C) charged	angered	howled

14   Stanley **IMPLORED** his brother to leave the room.

A	B	C	D	E
(A) demanded	asked	requested	urged	commanded

15   He felt **OBLIGED** to help the elderly woman cross the street.

A	B	C	D	E
force	regretful	obstructed	necessary	compelled

16   The students **CONSENTED** to the changes made to the school uniform.

A	B	C	D	E
agreed	objected	praised	pursued	protested

17   Tina **DISTRIBUTED** the slices of watermelon amongst her friends.

A	B	C	D	E
monopolised	combined	contributed	apportioned	withheld

18   She made an **IMPULSIVE** decision to buy the handbag.

A	B	C	D	E
impromptu	sensible	rational	cautious	informed

19   Niki's mother grew more **EXASPERATED** as she continued to rebel.

A	B	C	D	E
tranquil	gratified	blissful	frustrated	disconsolate

20   The foreshadowing of events in the film was cleverly **EXECUTED**.

A	B	C	D	E
beheaded	accomplished	predicted	published	prophesised

FIRST PAST THE POST®

Synonyms:

Similar Words

Test 3

Total

/20

You have **8** minutes to complete this test of **20** questions.

Test 3 - Synonyms: Similar Words

Circle the letter corresponding to the word that is most similar in meaning to the word on the left.

Example				
	A	Ⓑ	C	D
antipathetic	love	hostile	confused	sympathetic

		A	B	C	D
1	**complicated**	compliance	convoluted	simplicity	convection
2	**appalling**	apparel	admirable	atrocious	applauding
3	**loyalty**	treachery	devotion	admiration	royalty
4	**dull**	dismal	bright	dubious	fluorescent
5	**regularity**	variation	discord	consistency	imbalance
6	**beginner**	practical	veteran	professional	novice
7	**arrest**	liberate	seize	release	appreciate
8	**presence**	existence	prerogative	agitation	distress
9	**permissible**	intolerable	prohibited	acceptable	admission

		A	**B**	**C**	**D**
10	shortage	plenty	ample	abundance	scarcity
11	initiate	terminate	indifferent	neglect	commence
12	audacity	modesty	temerity	timidity	yielding
13	reference	deference	commerce	recommendation	bibliography
14	aspiration	ambition	apathy	heinous	lurid
15	salute	salvation	greet	refute	ignorance
16	antique	modern	current	analytical	archaic
17	insulting	mannerly	infuriate	offensive	complimentary
18	dependable	reliable	uncertain	deplorable	unsteady
19	maximum	least	greatest	manifest	magnitude
20	hysteria	laughing	lament	hypothesise	frenzy

BLANK PAGE

FIRST PAST THE POST®

Antonyms:

Word Bank

Test 4

Total
/40

You have **10** minutes to complete this test of **40** questions.

Test 4 - Antonyms: Word Bank

Choose a word from the word bank that has the meaning least similar to the word on the left.

Word Bank				
faithful	build	reveal	loiter	conclude
improper	descend	notorious	dilemma	nibble
important	reckless	disregard	stationary	responsible
illogical	culprit	loathe	decipherable	biased

1	conceal	*reveal*	11	admire	_____
2	begin	*conclude*	12	solution	_____
3	hurry	*disregard*	13	victim	_____
4	destroy	_____	14	gobble	_____
5	disloyal	_____	15	illegible	_____
6	trivial	_____	16	reputable	_____
7	rational	_____	17	mobile	_____
8	soar	_____	18	unreliable	_____
9	cautious	_____	19	acknowledge	_____
10	decent	_____	20	impartial	_____

Word Bank

worthwhile	discord	segregated	expand	unknown
meagre	tragic	idle	peculiar	shallow
polite	expel	permanent	failure	sympathetic
inelegant	unforgiving	rapid	persist	notice

1 graceful _____

2 invite _____

3 temporary _____

4 harmony _____

5 slow _____

6 ignore _____

7 success _____

8 voluminous _____

9 famous _____

10 hesitate _____

11 active _____

12 futile _____

13 deep _____

14 hilarious _____

15 normal _____

16 tolerant _____

17 contract _____

18 apathetic _____

19 together _____

20 rude _____

BLANK PAGE

FIRST PAST THE POST®

Antonyms:

Sentence Completion

Test 5

Total
/20

You have **8** minutes to complete this test of **20** questions.

Test 5 - Antonyms: Sentence Completion

Circle the letter corresponding to the word that is least similar in meaning to the word IN CAPITALS in the sentence above.

Example	The boy decided it was time to **WORK**.				
	A	B	Ⓒ	D	E
	skip	dance	play	eat	write

1 They were **INSISTENT** about where to go on holiday.

	A	B	C	D	E
	adamant	uncompromising	indifferent	absolute	unrelenting

2 The train timetable was **IMPRECISE**.

	A	B	C	D	E
	accurate	estimated	loose	guessed	rough

3 We stayed at a hotel owned by a very **HOSPITABLE** couple.

	A	B	C	D	E
	hostile	accommodating	altruistic	tolerant	friendly

4 I have an **AMPLE** amount of cheese on my pizza.

	A	B	C	D	E
	free	insufficient	plenty	abundant	meagre

5 The couple were found to be **COMPATIBLE**.

	A	B	C	D	E
	amicable	peaceful	unsuitable	congenial	shrill

6 They could see **BRAVERY** in her eyes.

	A	B	C	D	E
	fear	scared	guts	determination	valour

7   The interviewer was surprised at the medallist's **CONCEITED** nature.

A	B	C	D	E
concerned	boastful	pompous	self-effacing	pretentious

8   The bank's funds were **DIMINISHING** every day.

A	B	C	D	E
reduction	growing	disappearance	consumption	exhaustion

9   Jason **ADMITTED** that he took the last doughnut.

A	B	C	D	E
confessed	agreed	confirmed	denied	explained

10   Tammy was **OBSESSED** with her new book.

A	B	C	D	E
disenchanted	captivated	taken	gripped	addicted

11   At the end of the performance, the **EXCITED** crowd left the concert.

A	B	C	D	E
thrilled	raucous	boisterous	enthusiastic	disinterested

12   Graham was **DISHEARTENED** by his test score.

A	B	C	D	E
dismayed	dispirited	inspired	downcast	listless

13   Milo looked **DISTRESSED** before the exam.

A	B	C	D	E
inattentive	unsettled	dissatisfied	relaxed	fidgety

14   The **PRESTIGIOUS** music academy was always striving to be better.

A	B	C	D	E
esteemed	disreputable	famed	renowned	distinguished

15 It was a **FOOLISH** decision for the company.

A	B	C	D	E
logical	ill-advised	nonsensical	absurd	preposterous

16 The dresses worn by the women who attended the party were **EXTRAVAGANT**.

A	B	C	D	E
flamboyant	grandiose	ornate	fanciful	simple

17 Tom's attitude will **HINDER** the progress of this project.

A	B	C	D	E
prevent	advance	obstruct	stunt	delay

18 The **PASSIONATE** chef used lots of garlic in his cooking.

A	B	C	D	E
uninspired	inventive	gifted	accomplished	masterly

19 Jay's boss had given him **AMBIGUOUS** instructions.

A	B	C	D	E
random	clear	vague	unhelpful	hazy

20 My maths teacher is **SENSIBLE**.

A	B	C	D	E
insensible	irrational	realistic	reasonable	practical

FIRST PAST THE POST®

Antonyms:

Opposite Words

Test 6

Total
/40

You have **8** minutes to complete this test of **20** questions.

Test 6 - Antonyms: Opposite Words

Circle the letter corresponding to the word that is least similar in meaning to the word on the left.

Example				
	A	Ⓑ	C	D
object	item	agree	reject	artefact

		A	B	C	D
1	aspiration	apathy	astute	hope	imagination
2	minute	small	miniscule	substantial	minister
3	avoidable	adhere	aviation	avid	inevitable
4	imitation	fraud	original	irrigation	implication
5	begin	cease	start	beguile	bereavement
6	obey	listen	obligation	rebel	coherent
7	opponent	apparent	instigate	stifle	ally
8	tragedy	tremor	comedy	transfix	deter
9	perpetual	temporary	ongoing	perplexed	perforate

		A	**B**	**C**	**D**
10	**excessive**	plenty	expiry	moderate	exonerate
11	**exact**	extract	inaccurate	express	calm
12	**admire**	advertise	advocate	loathe	lurid
13	**random**	methodical	caress	mention	measure
14	**irresistible**	institution	irradiate	estimate	unappealing
15	**compulsory**	continuity	optional	impulsive	countenance
16	**perturbed**	perused	assonance	composed	perfectionist
17	**deprive**	satiate	volatile	insatiable	volume
18	**expose**	reveal	revel	wither	cover
19	**obscure**	enquire	quest	illuminate	observe
20	**deny**	defy	accept	salvation	denote

BLANK PAGE

FIRST PAST THE POST®

Word Definitions

Test 7

Total

/40

You have **15** minutes to complete this test of **40** questions.

Test 7 - Word Definitions

Circle the letter corresponding to the word that best fits the definition above.

Example	to smile widely				
	A	B	Ⓒ	D	E
	laugh	frown	grin	glower	sneer

1 a modest or low view of one's importance

A	B	C	D
humanity	humility	shame	moderate

2 severe or strict in manner

A	B	C	D
austere	prosperous	severity	willing

3 to annoy someone

A	B	C	D
analytical	tickle	try	vex

4 a passionate expression of grief

A	B	C	D
sorrowful	lament	stress	afraid

5 straightforward and frank in manner

A	B	C	D
rude	polite	candid	ambitious

6 a feeling of vague longing

A	B	C	D
wistfulness	grandiose	witty	cheeky

7   sturdy and durable in manner

A	B	C	D
duration	robust	brutal	deliberate

8   a peaceful or picturesque feeling

A	B	C	D
satisfying	artistic	tranquilise	idyllic

9   a great energy in pursuit of a cause

A	B	C	D
fanatic	crafty	authority	zeal

10   an extreme tiredness

A	B	C	D
rest	fatigue	elation	exhaust

11   to pretend to be affected by

A	B	C	D
officiate	faint	devise	feign

12   a strange or unsettling quality

A	B	C	D
uncanny	underhand	conceit	unkempt

13   a nervous manner

A	B	C	D
temerity	disarray	timorous	obstinate

14   the feeling of taking offense

A	B	C	D
caustic	umbrage	felony	insult

15 the quality of excessive confidence

A	B	C	D
temerity	timorous	honest	exaggerate

16 with a thick, sticky consistency

A	B	C	D
consistent	vicious	creamy	viscous

17 hostile or aggressive in manner

A	B	C	D
stern	nervous	belligerent	competent

18 having no real purpose or value

A	B	C	D
thoughtless	frivolous	committed	significant

19 disgusting in manner

A	B	C	D
repugnant	loutish	delicate	decease

20 boring and uninteresting in manner

A	B	C	D
serene	slick	insipid	captivating

21 to push or bump against someone

A	B	C	D
uncharitable	slide	jostle	dash

22 the quality of faithfulness to a person or belief

A	B	C	D
fidelity	communicate	fiendish	fidgety

23 having a cruel disregard for others

A	B	C	D
aggressive	callous	creative	tame

24 to treat someone disrespectfully

A	B	C	D
outrage	uncivil	cater	degrade

25 a short period of relief

A	B	C	D
delve	brief	respite	premise

26 an award or official recognition

A	B	C	D
achievement	prose	accolade	protection

27 to get worse over time

A	B	C	D
frustrate	fester	irregular	exude

28 a state of political and social disorder

A	B	C	D
tactic	slapdash	anarchy	inconsistent

29 to exchange without money

A	B	C	D
occupy	barter	deteriorate	hassle

30 the floor of a fireplace

A	B	C	D
detritus	wheel	basin	hearth

31 to cut off or restrict

A	B	C	D
supersede	curtail	overcome	complete

32 to deliberately avoid or reject

A	B	C	D
eschew	dispose	disconnect	elect

33 to regard with disgust

A	B	C	D
adore	attain	abhor	refrain

34 old-fashioned in manner

A	B	C	D
shady	fickle	archaic	befuddled

35 a huge and monstrous thing

A	B	C	D
berth	ultimate	community	behemoth

36 dirty or neglected in manner

A	B	C	D
squalid	disappointed	gregarious	severe

37 a subtle difference

A	B	C	D
libretto	nuance	frill	fluke

38 to obtain or get something

A	B	C	D
save	diminish	procure	frequent

39 a feeling of strong dislike

A	B	C	D
corrupt	tremble	animosity	nurture

40 unpleasantly bitter in   unpleasantly bitter in   unpleasantly bitter in   unpleasantly bitter in

A	B	C	D
lucid	arid	sickly	acrid

FIRST PAST THE POST®

Category Fit

Test 8

Total
/40

You have **10** minutes to complete this test of **40** questions.

Test 8 - Category Fit

Circle the letter corresponding to the category to which the word best belongs.

Example				
	A	Ⓑ	C	D
diamond	clothing	gemstone	food	drink

		A	B	C	D
1	checked	water	pattern	chocolate	person

		A	B	C	D
2	vinegar	condiment	drink	food	medicine

		A	B	C	D
3	mahogany	emotion	wood	furniture	vegetable

		A	B	C	D
4	mercury	thermometer	blue	challenge	metal

		A	B	C	D
5	French	language	art	currency	country

		A	B	C	D
6	calligraphy	English	writing	sign	book

		A	B	C	D
7	mare	feeling	animal	clothing	weapon

		A	B	C	D
8	flint	fire	rock	machine	ruby

		A	B	C	D
9	ukulele	song	music	note	instrument

		A	B	C	D
10	gargoyle	statue	animal	human	bat
11	lychee	sport	country	fruit	language
12	sleet	building	weather	furniture	jumper
13	cardamom	wood	sport	greeting	spice
14	tuber	jump	plant	joke	country
15	ciabatta	bread	ship	restaurant	coffee
16	cactus	office	map	computer	plant
17	husky	coat	dog	hat	drum
18	dinghy	game	candle	boat	wave
19	viper	dance	snake	tent	soil
20	lizard	reptile	fish	mammal	bird
21	penny	pig	coin	sweet	cupboard

		A	B	C	D
22	diabetes	chemical	disease	farm	charity
23	satchel	plastic	mountain	time	bag
24	atlas	house	stone	feast	book
25	lung	organ	piano	smoke	robbery
26	trout	sign	fish	light	frog
27	canine	bean	transport	tooth	calculator
28	tagliatelle	razor	software	pasta	bird
29	macaroon	cheese	toy	coat	biscuit
30	pestle	tool	sauce	sport	art
31	rumba	drink	dance	holiday	key
32	leech	fruit	song	worm	design
33	choir	ensemble	train	material	tournament

		A	**B**	**C**	**D**
34	**centaur**	valley	science	creature	vehicle
35	**soliloquy**	sand	novel	game	speech
36	**thatched**	dream	cloud	space	roof
37	**opera**	cinema	entertainment	castle	jungle
38	**poncho**	garment	toy	lake	hair
39	**soirée**	body-part	party	fire	food
40	**tartan**	sauce	juice	card	fabric

BLANK PAGE

FIRST PAST THE POST®

Mixed Test

Test 9

Total
/60

You have **17** minutes to complete this test of **60** questions.

Test 9 - Mixed Test - Synonyms: Word Bank

Choose a word from the word bank that has the meaning most similar to the word on the left.

Word Bank				
content	unfortunate	sympathy	ravenous	quiver
devilish	diligent	massacre	threatening	turbulent
defective	ponder	stubborn	devious	luxurious
pragmatic	diversity	enticing	hinder	necessary

1	meticulous	_____	11	unlucky	_____
2	cunning	_____	12	menacing	_____
3	satisfied	_____	13	tumultuous	_____
4	tremble	_____	14	contemplate	_____
5	carnage	_____	15	fiendish	_____
6	famished	_____	16	compassion	_____
7	faulty	_____	17	opulent	_____
8	essential	_____	18	tempting	_____
9	obstinate	_____	19	variety	_____
10	impede	_____	20	realistic	_____

Choose a word from the word bank that has the meaning least similar to the word on the left.

Word Bank				
poverty	optional	captive	advanced	calm
careless	quiet	dim	please	common
stable	haphazard	brave	harsh	thoughtful
lenient	clamour	boundless	modest	effortless

1	fearful	_____	11	wealth	_____
2	disappoint	_____	12	free	_____
3	rudimentary	_____	13	organised	_____
4	limited	_____	14	bright	_____
5	rare	_____	15	careful	_____
6	ostentatious	_____	16	strict	_____
7	raucous	_____	17	obligatory	_____
8	silence	_____	18	livid	_____
9	inconsiderate	_____	19	fluctuating	_____
10	strenuous	_____	20	mild	_____

Test 9 - Mixed Test - Synonyms: Sentence Completion

Circle the letter corresponding to the word that is most similar in meaning to the word IN CAPITALS in the sentence above.

1   The **FRAGRANT** flowers were placed in a vase in the living room.

A	B	C	D	E
nice	colourful	exotic	aromatic	noxious

2   The old photographs stirred up feelings of **NOSTALGIA**.

A	B	C	D	E
appreciative	ungrateful	sentimentality	blessed	jubilant

3   Joe needed a break after the **HEATED** discussion.

A	B	C	D	E
dull	warm	loving	passionate	digressive

4   He **PREVENTED** himself from eating the biscuits.

A	B	C	D	E
possibly	previewed	allow	restrained	force

5   The team were **TENACIOUS** in their pursuit of victory.

A	B	C	D	E
persistent	weak	candid	bored	lacklustre

6   The rules of the game were **RIGID**.

A	B	C	D	E
slack	inflexible	lenient	bendy	easy

7   I was unable to **DISCLOSE** the information.

A	B	C	D	E
pretend	ascend	reveal	hide	conceal

8   I had to **CREATE** more content for the book.

A	B	C	D	E
destroy	defer	cascade	dismantle	generate

9   I did not **UNDERSTAND** the instructions.

A	B	C	D	E
practice	unfold	journey	comprehend	exclude

10   This was a **GENUINE** piece of art.

A	B	C	D	E
legitimate	fake	unimaginative	ugly	irksome

Test 9 - Mixed Test - Category Fit

Circle the letter corresponding to the category to which the word best belongs.

		A	B	C	D
1	**tram**	transport	dilemma	wig	button
2	**calico**	cat	liquid	plastic	measurement
3	**squash**	container	sport	confectionary	book
4	**brooch**	hat	disaster	ornament	royalty
5	**maize**	treasure	fruit	plant	route
6	**helmet**	protection	museum	footwear	school
7	**flask**	parcel	liquid	container	confectionary
8	**arrow**	body organ	weapon	car part	wood
9	**codex**	book	string	film	instrument
10	**raven**	future	colour	hunger	bird

FIRST PAST THE POST®

Mixed Test

Test 10

Total

/60

You have **17** minutes to complete this test of **60** questions.

Test 10 - Mixed Test - Synonyms: Word Bank

Choose a word from the word bank that has the meaning most similar to the word on the left.

Word Bank				
energetic	squirm	glowing	cease	weak
nemesis	determined	articulate	fixation	mediocre
shy	abandon	bewilder	blazing	distrustful
attitude	notoriety	keen	defeated	apathetic

1	resolute	_____	11	stop	_____
2	indifferent	_____	12	infamy	_____
3	crestfallen	_____	13	radiant	_____
4	fragile	_____	14	ordinary	_____
5	obsession	_____	15	cynical	_____
6	active	_____	16	scorching	_____
7	well-spoken	_____	17	forsake	_____
8	meek	_____	18	eager	_____
9	writhe	_____	19	demeanour	_____
10	bemuse	_____	20	enemy	_____

Choose a word from the word bank that has the meaning least similar to the word on the left.

Word Bank				
personable	professional	criticise	blame	trivial
mellow	benevolent	dissatisfied	indulge	sophisticated
failure	harmless	sharp	desert	smooth
flawed	dear	begin	polite	dissuade

1	cruel	_____	11	satisfied	_____
2	important	_____	12	deadly	_____
3	abstain	_____	13	discourteous	_____
4	blunt	_____	14	compliment	_____
5	inhabit	_____	15	forgive	_____
6	conclude	_____	16	rough	_____
7	amateur	_____	17	unrefined	_____
8	persuade	_____	18	perfect	_____
9	haughty	_____	19	inexpensive	_____
10	angry	_____	20	triumph	_____

Test 10 - Mixed Test - Word Definitions

Circle the letter corresponding to the word that best fits the definition above.

1   to please by indulging

A	B	C	D
obtain	appraise	pander	panda

2   to express as an amount

A	B	C	D
measurement	volume	quantify	count

3   to justify

A	B	C	D
legal	lavish	judge	warrant

4   of central importance

A	B	C	D
fundamental	arched	partial	stable

5   to question something

A	B	C	D
request	doubtful	query	theory

6   to refuse to allow something

A	B	C	D
forbid	conclude	abolition	grumble

7   extremely sad or depressed in manner

A	B	C	D
pouch	buoyant	forlorn	downy

8   to begin or formally commence

A	B	C	D
attend	inaugurate	quarrel	correspond

9   a master of something

A	B	C	D
talisman	crusade	expert	exalt

10   entirely without harm or offense

A	B	C	D
novel	inevitable	innovative	innocuous

Test 10 - Mixed Test - Category Fit

Circle the letter corresponding to the category to which the word best belongs.

		A	B	C	D
1	**walled**	garden	salad	country	name
2	**bee**	honey	plant	insect	flower
3	**algebra**	mathematics	feeling	nature	biology
4	**rabbit**	animal	holiday	chocolate	carnivore
5	**their**	noun	adverb	pronoun	adjective
6	**hail**	adjective	precipitation	book	greenery
7	**trainers**	clothing	sport	footwear	equipment
8	**basil**	tree	film	vegetable	herb
9	**lipstick**	skincare	tool	cosmetic	colour
10	**museum**	playground	building	skeleton	geography

FIRST PAST THE POST®

Mixed Test

Test 11

Total
/60

You have **20** minutes to complete this test of **60** questions.

Test 11 - Mixed Test - Antonyms: Word Bank

Choose a word from the word bank that has the meaning least similar to the word on the left.

Word Bank				
strong	miserly	improve	moist	narrow
permit	end	clarify	entrap	verbose
uninterested	dawdle	lifeless	contempt	sabotage
apart	titter	cowardice	broad	free

1	feeble	_____	11	animated	_____
2	initiate	_____	12	hurry	_____
3	worsen	_____	13	inquisitive	_____
4	respect	_____	14	dry	_____
5	wide	_____	15	succinct	_____
6	ban	_____	16	together	_____
7	generous	_____	17	wail	_____
8	befuddle	_____	18	courage	_____
9	release	_____	19	thin	_____
10	support	_____	20	captive	_____

Test 11 - Mixed Test - Antonyms: Sentence Completion

Circle the letter corresponding to the word that is least similar in meaning to the word IN CAPITALS in the sentence above.

1   The decision proved to be **PIVOTAL**.

A	B	C	D	E
crucial	essential	insignificant	critical	momentous

2   The house at the end of the road has been **VACANT** for a few months.

A	B	C	D	E
abandoned	uninhabited	occupied	deserted	empty

3   During school, the children were **MISCHIEVOUS.**

A	B	C	D	E
playful	rogue	deceitful	obedient	frolicsome

4   He had always been a **GRACEFUL** dancer.

A	B	C	D	E
dignified	stylish	novel	beautiful	clumsy

5   The waiter was very **COURTEOUS**.

A	B	C	D	E
welcoming	impolite	polite	respectful	kind

6   She was a **PERMANENT** addition to the team.

A	B	C	D	E
lasting	eternal	temporary	enduring	indefinite

7   The field trip to Devon was **COMPULSORY**.

A	B	C	D	E
voluntary	mandatory	obligatory	spontaneous	necessary

8   The jury decided that the woman was **GUILTY**.

A	B	C	D	E
culpable	accountable	innocent	liable	free

9   The teacher was too **LENIENT**.

A	B	C	D	E
forgiving	sympathetic	strict	tolerant	indulgent

10   They were **PUBLIC** matters.

A	B	C	D	E
private	communal	general	collective	universal

Circle the letter corresponding to the word that is most similar in meaning to the word on the left.

		A	B	C	D
1	**convey**	consider	dissuade	convection	communicate
2	**destruction**	annihilation	development	reparation	destitute
3	**suggest**	deny	ingest	propose	conceal
4	**unnecessary**	intermittent	effortless	superfluous	disjointed
5	**release**	feasible	relive	relentless	discharge
6	**abnormal**	atypical	abhorrent	absence	communal
7	**confusion**	composure	clarity	befuddlement	orientation
8	**relate**	dissociate	associate	distinguish	suppress
9	**teamwork**	singular	swarm	tedious	collaboration
10	**flexible**	fester	fixate	pliant	precarious

		A	**B**	**C**	**D**
11	**delicious**	deliver	scrumptious	disenchanting	unappetising
12	**hidden**	hideous	obvious	concealed	apparent
13	**ask**	enquire	claim	repudiate	reply
14	**entertaining**	dull	enterprise	pertaining	amusing
15	**greet**	shun	address	disregard	slight
16	**difficult**	strenuous	facile	trivial	effortless
17	**frail**	hearty	incumbent	weak	brittle
18	**sustain**	susceptible	condemn	relay	maintain
19	**pause**	expedite	suspend	hasten	postulate
20	**jamboree**	celebration	reticent	preserve	brute

Test 11 - Mixed Test - Word Definitions

Circle the letter corresponding to the word that best fits the definition above.

1   to be overwhelmed

A	B	C	D
wrenched	inundated	overdone	undermined

2   a person or thing that lives in a place

A	B	C	D
inhibit	habitat	inhabitant	covet

3   the quality of not having a clear meaning

A	B	C	D
ambiguity	conflagration	futility	illusion

4   the quality of causing disgust

A	B	C	D
plague	torture	terrible	repulsive

5   bad-tempered in manner

A	B	C	D
hospitable	petulant	typical	assertive

6   to explain the details of something

A	B	C	D
explode	declare	debrief	pummel

7   of vital importance

A	B	C	D
aristocracy	adverse	bizarre	imperative

8   not easily noticed

A	B	C	D
oblivious	inconspicuous	conspicuous	obvious

9   requiring a lot of time and effort

A	B	C	D
laborious	lugubrious	monotonous	lunar

10   determined in manner

A	B	C	D
explosive	divest	resolute	ludicrous

FIRST PAST THE POST®

Mixed Test

Test 12

Total
/60

You have **20** minutes to complete this test of **60** questions.

Test 12 - Mixed Test - Synonyms: Word Bank

Choose a word from the word bank that has the meaning most similar to the word on the left.

Word Bank				
pardon	escape	charge	mourn	holy
engrossed	shunt	haggle	conceited	collude
progressively	valid	trick	perfume	dejected
plume	predicament	domain	stoop	border

1	relieve	_____	11	disheartened _____
2	jolt	_____	12	fringe _____
3	negotiate	_____	13	habitat _____
4	hoax	_____	14	gradually _____
5	sacred	_____	15	engaged _____
6	conspire	_____	16	attack _____
7	grieve	_____	17	egocentric _____
8	hunch	_____	18	fragrance _____
9	feather	_____	19	legitimate _____
10	flee	_____	20	dilemma _____

Test 12 - Mixed Test - Antonyms: Opposite Words

Circle the letter corresponding to the word that is least similar in meaning to the word on the left.

		A	B	C	D
1	**horizontal**	horizon	fertile	legion	vertical
2	**active**	zealous	idle	energetic	agile
3	**tame**	temerity	tamper	wild	wilderness
4	**plentiful**	plough	sparse	spatial	repel
5	**wealth**	postulate	weather	scarcity	pondering
6	**destroy**	courtesy	create	delegate	damage
7	**simplicity**	grandeur	petite	awkward	dainty
8	**compliment**	endorsement	candid	confident	insult
9	**victory**	defeat	truncate	deplete	triumph
10	**common**	compliment	unify	union	unique

		A	B	C	D
11	transparent	translucent	glassy	opaque	dark
12	dusk	dark	dawn	gloomy	dim
13	powerful	weak	lenient	authoritative	dominant
14	captivity	liberty	stout	captivating	capacity
15	sharp	needle	blunder	unintelligent	shallow
16	dismal	derogatory	cheerful	dreary	light
17	solitude	friend	companionship	alone	seclude
18	project	eject	mumble	proceed	file
19	indulge	dry	deprive	construct	quaint
20	aid	ascent	hinder	subsidise	assist

Test 12 - Mixed Test - Word Definitions

Circle the letter corresponding to the word that best fits the definition above.

1   an inconvenience

A	B	C	D
vocation	bolster	pledge	nuisance

2   the act of working together

A	B	C	D
cooperation	alliteration	contradiction	compliment

3   to set free

A	B	C	D
placate	incarcerate	liberate	obstinate

4   lacking sophistication or crude in manner

A	B	C	D
jovial	vulgar	cruelty	voluptuous

5   to die or disintegrate

A	B	C	D
perish	devastating	correlate	divide

6   the feeling of being disappointed

A	B	C	D
refined	browbeaten	contrite	crestfallen

7   lacking in what is necessary or required

A	B	C	D
incessant	inefficient	insufficient	indifferent

8 the quality of appearing composed

A	B	C	D
spasm	poise	possessed	immobile

9 a wild excitement

A	B	C	D
conflagration	viral	frenzy	expression

10 requiring immediate action or attention

A	B	C	D
urgent	active	hysterical	sinister

Test 12 - Mixed Test - Category Fit

Circle the letter corresponding to the category to which the word best belongs.

		A	B	C	D
1	**deodorant**	toiletry	detergent	powder	air
2	**magpie**	seafood	clothing	food	bird
3	**sycamore**	town	flower	tree	fly
4	**lobster**	net	seafood	shell	rock
5	**cotton**	mineral	plant	furniture	herb
6	**monocle**	bicycle	metal	eyewear	car
7	**spade**	sea	shell	hearts	tool
8	**minotaur**	dinosaur	creature	goat	bull
9	**tap**	swing	sink	dance	water
10	**yoga**	game	exercise	yoghurt	health

BLANK PAGE

Answers

Test 1 - Synonyms: Word Bank

Question	Answer
1	NEAT and **IMMACULATE**
2	YELL and **HOWL**
3	PUTRID and **ROTTEN**
4	CHEERFUL and **JAUNTY**
5	ABRUPT and **SUDDEN**
6	STRIVE and **AIM**
7	WISE and **KNOWLEDGEABLE**
8	FIND and **LOCATE**
9	FRAGRANT and **AROMATIC**
10	DIVERGE and **DEVIATE**
11	PECULIAR and **BIZARRE**
12	WICKED and **VILLAINOUS**
13	FREIGHT and **CARGO**
14	SOMBRE and **MELANCHOLY**
15	SOPHISTICATED and **REFINED**
16	VICIOUS and **BRUTAL**
17	VIVID and **INTENSE**
18	TRIUMPH and **SUCCESS**
19	GENUINE and **AUTHENTIC**
20	CATEGORY and **CLASSIFICATION**

Test 1 - Synonyms: Word Bank

Question	Answer
1	AGGRIEVED and **INDIGNANT**
2	SWIFT and **NIMBLE**
3	RESPECTFUL and **DEFERENTIAL**
4	AGGRESSIVE and **BELLIGERENT**
5	EMULATE and **MIMIC**
6	HEROIC and **COURAGEOUS**
7	IMPEDIMENT and **HINDRANCE**
8	DISGRACEFUL and **DEPLORABLE**
9	LUDICROUS and **ABSURD**
10	EXPUNGE and **OBLITERATE**
11	DEVASTATION and **DESOLATION**
12	OBLIGATORY and **NECESSARY**
13	EXPOSE and **UNCOVER**
14	FRUGAL and **THRIFTY**
15	EXCESS and **SURPLUS**
16	ELEGANT and **GRACEFUL**
17	GENIAL and **FRIENDLY**
18	MUNDANE and **MONOTONOUS**
19	NUTRITIOUS and **HEALTHY**
20	URGENT and **PRESSING**

Test 2 - Synonyms: Sentence Completion

Question	Answer	Explanation
1	E	**ANXIOUSLY**, Jerry entered the haunted house.
2	C	She **WIELDED** her sword in order to fight the dragon.
3	B	Their **PERSISTENT** squabbling meant that I had to leave the house.
4	D	Our ship had no support and was very **EXPOSED** to enemy fire.
5	A	I was **RESTLESS** so I decided to skip the queue.
6	C	The King's armour was very **ROBUST**.
7	E	I found it **HILARIOUS** that the clown tripped over.
8	D	The **ENTICING** aroma from the kitchen spread through the whole house.
9	A	I **STROLLED** through the woods before sunset.
10	D	Oscar **BARGAINED** with his father to be allowed to go to the party.
11	A	Lucy **ENDEAVOURED** to finish her coursework before the concert.
12	E	Daisy had a **FLICKER** of hope that her parents would let her adopt a kitten.
13	C	She **CHARGED** out of the room after the argument with her father.
14	D	Stanley **URGED** his brother to leave the room.
15	E	He felt **COMPELLED** to help the elderly woman cross the street.
16	A	The students **AGREED** to the changes made to the school uniform.
17	D	Tina **APPORTIONED** the slices of watermelon amongst her friends.
18	A	She made an **IMPROMPTU** decision to buy the handbag.
19	D	Niki's mother grew more **FRUSTRATED** as she continued to rebel.
20	B	The foreshadowing of events in the film was cleverly **ACCOMPLISHED**.

Test 3 - Synonyms: Similar Words

Question	Answer	Explanation
1	B	COMPLICATED and **CONVOLUTED**
2	C	APPALLING and **ATROCIOUS**
3	B	LOYALTY and **DEVOTION**
4	A	DULL and **DISMAL**
5	C	REGULARITY and **CONSISTENCY**
6	D	BEGINNER and **NOVICE**
7	B	ARREST and **SEIZE**
8	A	PRESENCE and **EXISTENCE**
9	C	PERMISSIBLE and **ACCEPTABLE**
10	D	SHORTAGE and **SCARCITY**
11	D	INITIATE and **COMMENCE**
12	B	AUDACITY and **TEMERITY**
13	C	REFERENCE and **RECOMMENDATION**
14	A	ASPIRATION and **AMBITION**
15	B	SALUTE and **GREET**
16	D	ANTIQUE and **ARCHAIC**
17	C	INSULTING and **OFFENSIVE**
18	A	DEPENDABLE and **RELIABLE**
19	B	MAXIMUM and **GREATEST**
20	D	HYSTERIA and **FRENZY**

Test 4 - Antonyms: Word Bank

Question	Answer
1	CONCEAL and **REVEAL**
2	BEGIN and **CONCLUDE**
3	HURRY and **LOITER**
4	DESTROY and **BUILD**
5	DISLOYAL and **FAITHFUL**
6	TRIVIAL and **IMPORTANT**
7	RATIONAL and **ILLOGICAL**
8	SOAR and **DESCEND**
9	CAUTIOUS and **RECKLESS**
10	DECENT and **IMPROPER**
11	ADMIRE and **LOATHE**
12	SOLUTION and **DILEMMA**
13	VICTIM and **CULPRIT**
14	GOBBLE and **NIBBLE**
15	ILLEGIBLE and **DECIPHERABLE**
16	REPUTABLE and **NOTORIOUS**
17	MOBILE and **STATIONARY**
18	UNRELIABLE and **RESPONSIBLE**
19	ACKNOWLEDGE and **DISREGARD**
20	IMPARTIAL and **BIASED**

Test 4 - Antonyms: Word Bank

Question	Answer
1	GRACEFUL and **INELEGANT**
2	INVITE and **EXPEL**
3	TEMPORARY and **PERMANENT**
4	HARMONY and **DISCORD**
5	SLOW and **RAPID**
6	IGNORE and **NOTICE**
7	SUCCESS and **FAILURE**
8	VOLUMINOUS and **MEAGRE**
9	FAMOUS and **UNKNOWN**
10	HESITATE and **PERSIST**
11	ACTIVE and **IDLE**
12	FUTILE and **WORTHWHILE**
13	DEEP and **SHALLOW**
14	HILARIOUS and **TRAGIC**
15	NORMAL and **PECULIAR**
16	TOLERANT and **UNFORGIVING**
17	CONTRACT and **EXPAND**
18	APATHETIC and **SYMPATHETIC**
19	TOGETHER and **SEGREGATED**
20	RUDE and **POLITE**

Test 5 - Antonyms: Sentence Completion

Question	Answer	Explanation
1	C	They were **INDIFFERENT** about where to go on holiday.
2	A	The train timetable was **ACCURATE**.
3	A	We stayed at a hotel owned by a very **HOSTILE** couple.
4	B	I have an **INSUFFICIENT** amount of cheese on my pizza.
5	C	The couple were found to be **UNSUITABLE**.
6	A	They could see **FEAR** in her eyes.
7	D	The interviewer was surprised at the medallist's **SELF-EFFACING** nature.
8	B	The bank's funds were **GROWING** every day.
9	D	Jason **DENIED** that he took the last doughnut.
10	A	Tammy was **DISENCHANTED** with her new book.
11	E	At the end of the performance, the **DISINTERESTED** crowd left the concert.
12	C	Graham was **INSPIRED** by his test score.
13	D	Milo looked **RELAXED** before the exam.
14	B	The **DISREPUTABLE** music academy was always striving to be better.
15	A	It was a **LOGICAL** decision for the company.
16	E	The dresses worn by the women who attended the party were **SIMPLE**.
17	B	Tom's attitude will **ADVANCE** the progress of this project.
18	A	The **UNINSPIRED** chef used lots of garlic in his cooking.
19	B	Jay's boss had given him **CLEAR** instructions.
20	B	My maths teacher is **IRRATIONAL**.

Test 6 - Antonyms: Opposite Words

Question	Answer	Explanation
1	A	ASPIRATION and **APATHY**
2	C	MINUTE and **SUBSTANTIAL**
3	D	AVOIDABLE and **INEVITABLE**
4	B	IMITATION and **ORIGINAL**
5	A	BEGIN and **CEASE**
6	C	OBEY and **REBEL**
7	D	OPPONENT and **ALLY**
8	B	TRAGEDY and **COMEDY**
9	A	PERPETUAL and **TEMPORARY**
10	C	EXCESSIVE and **MODERATE**
11	B	EXACT and **INACCURATE**
12	C	ADMIRE and **LOATHE**
13	A	RANDOM and **METHODICAL**
14	D	IRRESISTIBLE and **UNAPPEALING**
15	B	COMPULSORY and **OPTIONAL**
16	C	PERTURBED and **COMPOSED**
17	A	DEPRIVE and **SATIATE**
18	D	EXPOSE and **COVER**
19	C	OBSCURE and **ILLUMINATE**
20	B	DENY and **ACCEPT**

Test 7 – Word Definitions

Question	Answer	Explanation
1	B	a modest or low view of ones importance: **HUMILITY**
2	A	severe or strict in manner: **AUSTERE**
3	D	to annoy someone: **VEX**
4	B	a passionate expression of grief: **LAMENT**
5	C	straightforward and frank in manner: **CANDID**
6	A	a feeling of vague longing: **WISTFULNESS**
7	B	sturdy and durable in manner: **ROBUST**
8	D	a peaceful or picturesque feeling: **IDYLLIC**
9	D	a great energy in pursuit of a cause: **ZEAL**
10	B	an extreme tiredness: **FATIGUE**
11	D	to pretend to be affected by: **FEIGN**
12	A	a strange or unsettling quality: **UNCANNY**
13	C	having a nervous manner: **TIMOROUS**
14	B	the feeling of taking offense: **UMBRAGE**
15	A	the quality of excessive confidence: **TEMERITY**
16	D	with a thick, sticky consistency: **VISCOUS**
17	C	hostile or aggressive in manner: **BELLIGERENT**
18	B	having no real purpose or value: **FRIVOLOUS**
19	A	disgusting in manner: **REPUGNANT**
20	C	boring and uninteresting in manner: **INSIPID**
21	C	to push or bump against someone: **JOSTLE**
22	A	the quality of faithfulness to a person or belief: **FIDELITY**
23	B	having a cruel disregard for others: **CALLOUS**
24	D	to treat someone disrespectfully: **DEGRADE**
25	C	a short period of relief: **RESPITE**
26	C	an award or official recognition: **ACCOLADE**
27	B	to get worse over time: **FESTER**
28	C	a state of political and social disorder: **ANARCHY**
29	B	to exchange without money: **BARTER**
30	D	the floor of a fireplace: **HEARTH**
31	B	to cut off or restrict: **CURTAIL**
32	A	to deliberately avoid or reject: **ESCHEW**
33	C	to regard with disgust: **ABHOR**
34	C	old-fashioned in manner: **ARCHAIC**
35	D	a huge and monstrous thing: **BEHEMOTH**
36	A	dirty or neglected in manner: **SQUALID**
37	B	a subtle difference: **NUANCE**
38	C	to obtain or get something: **PROCURE**
39	C	a feeling of strong dislike: **ANIMOSITY**
40	D	unpleasantly bitter in taste or smell: **ACRID**

Test 8 – Category Fit

Question	Answer	Explanation
1	B	CHECKED: **pattern**
2	A	VINEGAR: **condiment**
3	B	MAHOGANY: **wood**
4	D	MERCURY: **metal**
5	A	FRENCH: **language**
6	B	CALLIGRAPHY: **writing**
7	B	MARE: **animal**
8	B	FLINT: **rock**
9	D	UKULELE: **instrument**
10	A	GARGOYLE: **statue**
11	C	LYCHEE: **fruit**
12	B	SLEET: **weather**
13	D	CARDAMOM: **spice**
14	B	TUBER: **plant**
15	A	CIABATTA: **bread**
16	D	CACTUS: **plant**
17	B	HUSKY: **dog**
18	C	DINGHY: **boat**
19	B	VIPER: **snake**
20	A	LIZARD: **reptile**
21	B	PENNY: **coin**
22	B	DIABETES: **disease**
23	D	SATCHEL: **bag**
24	D	ATLAS: **book**
25	A	LUNG: **organ**
26	B	TROUT: **fish**
27	C	CANINE: **tooth**
28	C	TAGLIATELLE: **pasta**
29	D	MACAROON: **biscuit**
30	A	PESTLE: **tool**
31	B	RUMBA: **dance**
32	C	LEECH: **worm**
33	A	CHOIR: **ensemble**
34	C	CENTAUR: **creature**
35	D	SOLILOQUY: **speech**
36	D	THATCHED: **roof**
37	B	OPERA: **entertainment**
38	A	PONCHO: **garment**
39	B	SOIRÉE: **party**
40	D	TARTAN: **fabric**

Test 9 - Mixed Test

Synonyms: Word Bank

Question	Answer
1	METICULOUS and **DILIGENT**
2	CUNNING and **DEVIOUS**
3	SATISFIED and **CONTENT**
4	TREMBLE and **QUIVER**
5	CARNAGE and **MASSACRE**
6	FAMISHED and **RAVENOUS**
7	FAULTY and **DEFECTIVE**
8	ESSENTIAL and **NECESSARY**
9	OBSTINATE and **STUBBORN**
10	IMPEDE and **HINDER**
11	UNLUCKY and **UNFORTUNATE**
12	MENACING and **THREATENING**
13	TUMULTUOUS and **TURBULENT**
14	CONTEMPLATE and **PONDER**
15	FIENDISH and **DEVILISH**
16	COMPASSION and **SYMPATHY**
17	OPULENT and **LUXURIOUS**
18	TEMPTING and **ENTICING**
19	VARIETY and **DIVERSITY**
20	REALISTIC and **PRAGMATIC**

Antonyms: Word Bank

Question	Answer
1	FEARFUL and **BRAVE**
2	DISAPPOINT and **PLEASE**
3	RUDIMENTARY and **ADVANCED**
4	LIMITED and **BOUNDLESS**
5	RARE and **COMMON**
6	OSTENTATIOUS and **MODEST**
7	RAUCOUS and **QUIET**
8	SILENCE and **CLAMOUR**
9	INCONSIDERATE and **THOUGHTFUL**
10	STRENUOUS and **EFFORTLESS**
11	WEALTH and **POVERTY**
12	FREE and **CAPTIVE**
13	ORGANISED and **HAPHAZARD**
14	BRIGHT and **DIM**
15	CAREFUL and **CARELESS**
16	STRICT and **LENIENT**
17	OBLIGATORY and **OPTIONAL**
18	LIVID and **CALM**
19	FLUCTUATING and **STABLE**
20	MILD and **HARSH**

Synonyms: Sentence Completion

Question	Answer	Explanation
1	D	The **AROMATIC** flowers were placed in a vase in the living room.
2	C	The old photographs stirred up feelings of **SENTIMENTALITY**.
3	D	Joe needed a break after the **PASSIONATE** discussion.
4	D	He **RESTRAINED** himself from eating the biscuits.
5	A	The team were **PERSISTENT** in their pursuit of victory.
6	B	The rules of the game were **INFLEXIBLE**.
7	C	I was unable to **REVEAL** the information.
8	E	I had to **GENERATE** more content for the book.
9	D	I did not **COMPREHEND** the instructions.
10	A	This was a **LEGITIMATE** piece of art.

Category Fit

Question	Answer	Explanation
1	A	TRAM: **transport**
2	A	CALICO: **cat**
3	B	SQUASH: **sport**
4	C	BROOCH: **ornament**
5	C	MAIZE: **plant**
6	A	HELMET: **protection**
7	C	FLASK: **container**
8	B	ARROW: **weapon**
9	A	CODEX: **book**
10	D	RAVEN: **bird**

Test 10 - Mixed Test

Synonyms: Word Bank

Question	Answer
1	RESOLUTE and **DETERMINED**
2	INDIFFERENT and **APATHETIC**
3	CRESTFALLEN and **DEFEATED**
4	FRAGILE and **WEAK**
5	OBSESSION and **FIXATION**
6	ACTIVE and **ENERGETIC**
7	WELL-SPOKEN and **ARTICULATE**
8	MEEK and **SHY**
9	WRITHE and **SQUIRM**
10	BEMUSE and **BEWILDER**
11	STOP and **CEASE**
12	INFAMY and **NOTORIETY**
13	RADIANT and **GLOWING**
14	ORDINARY and **MEDIOCRE**
15	CYNICAL and **DISTRUSTFUL**

Synonyms: Word Bank

Question	Answer
16	SCORCHING and **BLAZING**
17	FORSAKE and **ABANDON**
18	EAGER and **KEEN**
19	DEMEANOR and **ATTITUDE**
20	ENEMY and **NEMESIS**

Antonyms: Word Bank

Question	Answer
1	CRUEL and **BENEVOLENT**
2	IMPORTANT and **TRIVIAL**
3	ABSTAIN and **INDULGE**
4	BLUNT and **SHARP**
5	INHABIT and **DESERT**
6	CONCLUDE and **BEGIN**
7	AMATEUR and **PROFESSIONAL**
8	PERSUADE and **DISSUADE**
9	HAUGHTY and **PERSONABLE**
10	ANGRY and **MELLOW**
11	SATISFIED and **DISSATISFIED**
12	DEADLY and **HARMLESS**
13	DISCOURTEOUS and **POLITE**
14	COMPLIMENT and **CRITICISE**
15	FORGIVE and **BLAME**
16	ROUGH and **SMOOTH**
17	UNREFINED and **SOPHISTICATED**
18	PERFECT and **FLAWED**
19	INEXPENSIVE and **DEAR**
20	TRIUMPH and **FAILURE**

Word Definitions

Question	Answer	Explanation
1	C	to please by indulging: **PANDER**
2	C	to express as an amount: **QUANTIFY**
3	D	to justify: **WARRANT**
4	A	of central importance: **FUNDAMENTAL**
5	C	to question something: **QUERY**
6	A	to refuse to allow something: **FORBID**
7	C	extremely sad or depressed in manner: **FORLORN**
8	B	to begin or formally commence: **INAUGURATE**
9	C	a master of something: **EXPERT**
10	D	entirely without harm or offense: **INNOCUOUS**

Category Fit

Question	Answer	Explanation
1	A	WALLED: **garden**
2	C	BEE: **insect**
3	A	ALGEBRA: **mathematics**
4	A	RABBIT: **animal**
5	C	THEIR: **pronoun**
6	B	HAIL: **precipitation**
7	C	TRAINERS: **footwear**
8	D	BASIL: **herb**
9	C	LIPSTICK: **cosmetic**
10	B	MUSEUM: **building**

Test 11 - Mixed Test

Antonyms: Word Bank

Question	Answer
1	FEEBLE and **STRONG**
2	INITIATE and **END**
3	WORSEN and **IMPROVE**
4	RESPECT and **CONTEMPT**
5	WIDE and **NARROW**
6	BAN and **PERMIT**
7	GENEROUS and **MISERLY**
8	BEFUDDLE and **CLARIFY**
9	RELEASE and **ENTRAP**
10	SUPPORT and **SABOTAGE**
11	ANIMATED and **LIFELESS**
12	HURRY and **DAWDLE**
13	INQUISITIVE and **UNINTERESTED**
14	DRY and **MOIST**
15	SUCCINCT and **VERBOSE**
16	TOGETHER and **APART**
17	WAIL and **TITTER**
18	COURAGE and **COWARDICE**
19	THIN and **BROAD**
20	CAPTIVE and **FREE**

Antonyms: Sentence Completion

Question	Answer	Explanation
1	C	The decision proved to be **INSIGNIFICANT**.
2	C	The house at the end of the road has been **OCCUPIED** for a few months.
3	D	During school, the children were **OBEDIENT.**
4	E	He had always been a **CLUMSY** dancer.
5	B	The waiter was very **IMPOLITE**.
6	C	She was a **TEMPORARY** addition to the team.
7	A	The field trip to Devon was **VOLUNTARY**.
8	C	The jury decided that the woman was **INNOCENT**.
9	C	The teacher was too **STRICT**.
10	A	They were **PRIVATE** matters.

Synonyms: Similar Words

Question	Answer	Explanation
1	D	CONVEY and **COMMUNICATE**
2	A	DESTRUCTION and **ANNIHILATION**
3	C	SUGGEST and **PROPOSE**
4	C	UNNECESSARY and **SUPERFLUOUS**
5	D	RELEASE and **DISCHARGE**
6	A	ABNORMAL and **ATYPICAL**
7	C	CONFUSION and **BEFUDDLEMENT**
8	B	RELATE and **ASSOCIATE**
9	D	TEAMWORK and **COLLABORATION**
10	C	FLEXIBLE and **PLIANT**
11	B	DELICIOUS and **SCRUMPTIOUS**
12	C	HIDDEN and **CONCEALED**
13	A	ASK and **ENQUIRE**
14	D	ENTERTAINING and **AMUSING**
15	B	GREET and **ADDRESS**
16	A	DIFFICULT and **STRENUOUS**
17	C	FRAIL and **WEAK**
18	D	SUSTAIN and **MAINTAIN**
19	B	PAUSE and **SUSPEND**
20	A	JAMBOREE and **CELEBRATION**

Word Definitions

Question	Answer	Explanation
1	B	to be overwhelmed: **INUNDATED**
2	C	a person or thing that lives in a place: **INHABITANT**
3	A	the quality of not having a clear meaning: **AMBIGUITY**
4	D	the quality of causing disgust: **REPULSIVE**
5	B	bad-tempered in manner: **PETULANT**
6	C	to explain the details of something: **DEBRIEF**
7	D	of vital importance: **IMPERATIVE**
8	B	not easily noticed: **INCONSPICUOUS**
9	A	requiring a lot of time and effort: **LABORIOUS**
10	C	determined in manner: **RESOLUTE**

Test 12 - Mixed Test

Synonyms: Word Bank

Question	Answer
1	RELIEVE and **PARDON**
2	JOLT and **SHUNT**
3	NEGOTIATE and **HAGGLE**
4	HOAX and **TRICK**
5	SACRED and **HOLY**
6	CONSPIRE and **COLLUDE**
7	GRIEVE and **MOURN**
8	HUNCH and **STOOP**
9	FEATHER and **PLUME**
10	FLEE and **ESCAPE**
11	DISHEARTENED and **DEJECTED**
12	FRINGE and **BORDER**
13	HABITAT and **DOMAIN**
14	GRADUALLY and **PROGRESSIVELY**
15	ENGAGED and **ENGROSSED**
16	ATTACK and **CHARGE**
17	EGOCENTRIC and **CONCEITED**
18	FRAGRANCE and **PERFUME**
19	LEGITIMATE and **VALID**
20	DILEMMA and **PREDICAMENT**

Antonyms: Opposite Words

Question	Answer	Explanation
1	D	HORIZONTAL and **VERTICAL**
2	B	ACTIVE and **IDLE**
3	C	TAME and **WILD**
4	B	PLENTIFUL and **SPARSE**

Antonyms: Opposite Words

5	C	WEALTH and **SCARCITY**
6	B	DESTROY and **CREATE**
7	A	SIMPLICITY and **GRANDEUR**
8	D	COMPLIMENT and **INSULT**
9	A	VICTORY and **DEFEAT**
10	D	COMMON and **UNIQUE**
11	C	TRANSPARENT and **OPAQUE**
12	B	DUSK and **DAWN**
13	A	POWERFUL and **WEAK**
14	A	CAPTIVITY and **LIBERTY**
15	C	SHARP and **UNINTELLIGENT**
16	B	DISMAL and **CHEERFUL**
17	B	SOLITUDE and **COMPANIONSHIP**
18	B	PROJECT and **MUMBLE**
19	B	INDULGE and **DEPRIVE**
20	B	AID and **HINDER**

Word Definitions

Question	Answer	Explanation
1	D	an inconvenience: **NUISANCE**
2	A	the act of working together: **COOPERATION**
3	C	to set free: **LIBERATE**
4	B	lacking sophistication or crude in manner: **VULGAR**
5	A	to die or disintegrate: **PERISH**
6	D	the feeling of being disappointed: **CRESTFALLEN**
7	C	lacking in what is necessary or required: **INSUFFICIENT**
8	B	the quality of appearing composed: **POISE**
9	C	a wild excitement: **FRENZY**
10	A	requiring immediate action or attention: **URGENT**

Category Fit

Question	Answer	Explanation
1	A	DEODORANT: **toiletry**
2	D	MAGPIE: **bird**
3	C	SYCAMORE: **tree**
4	B	LOBSTER: **seafood**
5	B	COTTON: **plant**
6	C	MONOCLE: **eyewear**
7	D	SPADE: **tool**
8	B	MINOTAUR: **creature**
9	C	TAP: **dance**
10	B	YOGA: **exercise**